MISSION NEW YORK

Author: Catherine Aragon
Designer: Nada Orlić

MISSION LOCATION:
NEW YORK CITY

CONTENTS

AFTER COMPLETING EACH MISSION, CHECK (√) THE BOX AND WRITE THE NUMBER OF POINTS EARNED.

AT THE END, WRITE THE TOTAL NUMBER OF POINTS HERE: ☐

ATTENTION: FUTURE SPECIAL AGENTS YOU AND CASE OFFICERS GROWNUPS

CONGRATULATIONS! THE SIA (SECRET INTERNATIONAL AGENCY) HAS SELECTED YOU AS A CANDIDATE TO BECOME A SPECIAL AGENT.

The SIA carries out important assignments, secretly collecting intelligence in all corners of the globe. ("Intelligence" is spy-speak for "information.") Currently, we are in dire need of agents. Many want to join us, but only a few have what it takes.

HOW WILL YOU PROVE YOU'RE READY TO JOIN THE MOST ELITE SPY AGENCY IN THE WORLD? You must complete a series of missions in New York City (NYC). Similar to a scavenger hunt (only better), these missions will require you to carry out challenging investigations and collect valuable intel (short for "intelligence"). For each mission, you'll earn points towards becoming a special agent.

YOUR ASSIGNMENT: TRAVEL TO NYC WITH YOUR TEAM, LED BY YOUR CASE OFFICER. (A case officer accompanies agents on missions. Your case officer is your parent or other trusted adult.) You must earn at least 150 points to become a SIA special agent.

-The mission list and mission scorecard are on page 1.

-Read the "Anytime Missions" early, so that you'll remain on alert and ready to earn points. You can complete these at any time during your stay.

-You don't need to complete all of the missions to reach 150 points or complete them in any particular order.

BONUS MISSION

Want even more New York fun? Visit **Scavengerhuntadventures.Com/bonus** (all lowercase) today to download your **free bonus mission: "CENTRAL PARK STATUES."**

(Plus, you'll get *The Museum Spy*, our free e-book!)

"Get Your Bonus Mission Today!"

MISSION RULES

- Be kind and respectful to team members.
- Your case officer (your parent or other trusted adult) has the final decision regarding point awards.
- Your case officer serves as the official "scorekeeper."
- Your case officer has the final decision on what missions will be attempted. (Don't worry, you can still earn enough points to become an agent without completing all the missions.)
- Always be on alert. You never know when a chance to earn points lies just around the corner.

TO CONCEAL THEIR REAL IDENTITIES, SPECIAL AGENTS ALWAYS USE CODE NAMES. FOR EXAMPLE, JAMES BOND'S CODE NAME IS 007. THINK OF YOUR OWN CODE NAME TO USE DURING YOUR MISSION IN NYC.

SIGN YOUR CODE NAME HERE:

....

____

DATE

Important: For the missions you will need a pen or pencil and a camera. **LET THE MISSIONS BEGIN - GOOD LUCK!**

PRE-ARRIVAL BRIEF

AGENTS MUST HAVE SHARP SKILLS WHEN IT COMES TO ANALYZING IMAGES, SUCH AS PHOTOS, IN ORDER TO GATHER IMPORTANT INTEL.

"Intel" is short for "intelligence." Aerial photos like this one are taken from high in the sky by a satellite, a machine that orbits the Earth and takes pictures. Governments sometimes use satellites for spying, and other times simply for gathering information.

A satellite snapped this photo of North America at night. The clusters of white light are night-time city lights.

my notes:

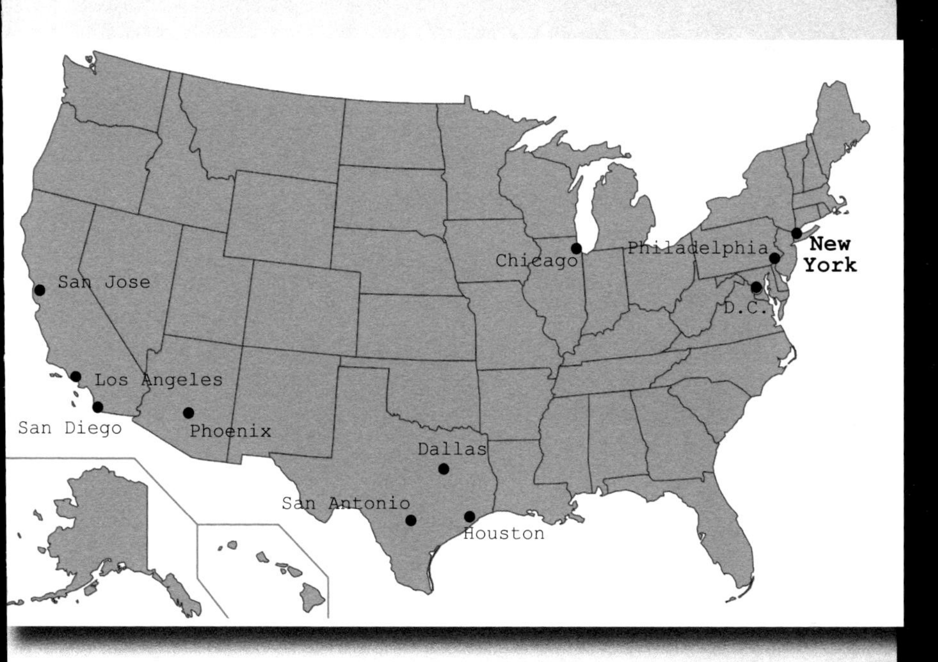

Examine the location of New York using the map. (The map contains the 10 largest U.S. cities, plus the nation's capital.) Then...

- [ ] **FIND NEW YORK ON THE SATELLITE PHOTO AND CIRCLE IT.** (Remember, large cities like New York will have the most lights.)

Can you make out any other cities on the satellite image?

MUSEUM OF NATURAL HISTORY

ONE OF THE TOP RULES OF SPYING: BLEND IN WITH YOUR SURROUNDINGS. YOU CAN NEVER SPOT THE BEST AGENTS, BECAUSE THEY DON'T LOOK LIKE AGENTS. HERE, THAT MEANS "PLAYING TOURIST" BY STROLLING AROUND THE MUSEUM.

- [ ] HUNT DOWN THE STATUE OF THIS MAN OUTSIDE THE MUSEUM. WHO IS IT?

The mystery man & his family

- MYSTERY MAN
- HIS QUOTES
- ENDANGERED SPECIES
- EXTINCT BIRD
- "LARGEST" ANIMAL HUNT
- FOSSILS
- MOAI FIGURE
- TONATIUH
- "LUCY"
- NATIVE AMERICAN FIGURINE
- COSMIC PATHWAY

This mystery man not only served as governor of New York, he also was the 26th president. He was ahead of his time in realizing the importance of protecting our environment. Venture inside to the museum's entrance hall.

☐ FIND THESE LINES FROM HIS FAMOUS QUOTES.

2 POINTS

"IT IS HARD TO FAIL BUT IT IS WORSE NEVER TO HAVE TRIED TO SUCCEED."

"THE NATION BEHAVES WELL IF IT TREATS THE NATURAL RESOURCES AS ASSETS* WHICH IT MUST TURN OVER TO THE NEXT GENERATION…"

This president felt so strongly about protecting the environment and wildlife that he set up our first National Wildlife Refuge - at a place called Pelican Island in Florida. The island provided a protected place for species of birds who, in the early 1900's, were being hunted for their feathers and might have become extinct. Hunters would kill the birds for their feathers, selling them to hat manufacturers (at twice the price per weight of gold) for "plume hats" - a fashion "must-have" of that era.

a plume hat

*asset = something valuable

As you explore the museum, keep a lookout for the endangered species display.

☐ **WHAT ARE THE LARGEST AND SMALLEST ANIMALS YOU FIND THAT ARE ENDANGERED?**

Find the skeleton of the bird which once lived on an island in the Indian Ocean, a species now extinct.

☐ **WHAT TYPE OF BIRD WAS IT?**

The museum is packed with animals claiming the title of "world's largest." **Remain on the lookout for the title-holders below.** (The animals in the museum may or may not appear exactly the same as the example photos.) **ONE POINT FOR EACH TYPE.**

☐ **BLUE WHALE** (largest animal)(above)

☐ **WHALE SHARK** (largest fish) (below)

☐ **MOOSE** (largest deer)

☐ **JAGUAR** (largest cat in the Americas)

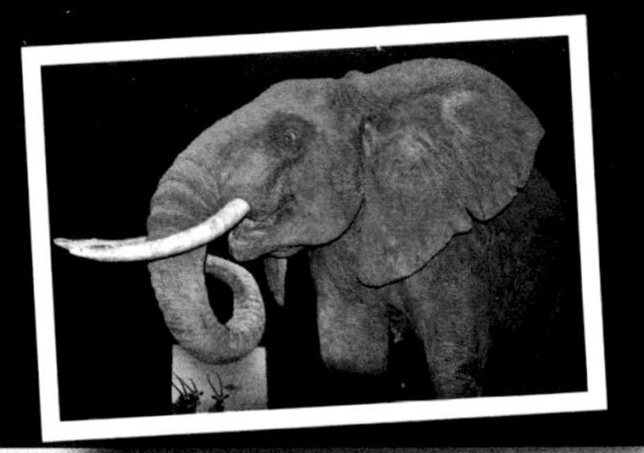

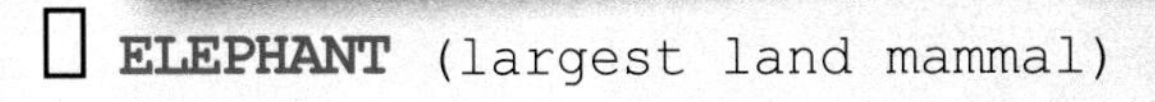
☐ **ELEPHANT** (largest land mammal)

☐ **OSTRICH** (largest bird)

☐ **KOMODO DRAGON** (largest lizard)

Examine the remains of ancient animals in the Fossil Halls.

☐ **WHICH THREE FOSSILS DO YOU THINK LOOK THE MOST THREATENING?**

3 POINTS

my notes:

☐ **HAVE YOUR PHOTO SNAPPED IN FRONT OF THE "MOAI" MODEL (SIMILAR TO THE ORIGINALS ABOVE).**

The island where these statues originate lies in a far southeast corner of the Pacific Ocean, around 2,000 miles west of Chile.

☐ **WHAT'S THE NAME OF THE ISLAND?**

☐ **UNCOVER "TONATIUH," THE AZTEC SUN GOD, AT THE CENTER OF AN AZTEC SUN STONE.**

☐ **BONUS: FIND ANOTHER VERSION OF TONATIUH, THIS TIME IN FULL-COLOR.**

my notes:

Track down the remains of "Lucy."

☐ **HOW OLD IS SHE?** 1 POINT

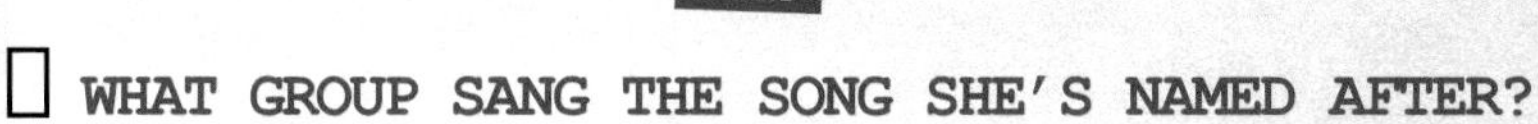

☐ **WHAT GROUP SANG THE SONG SHE'S NAMED AFTER?**

☐ **LOCATE THIS FIGURINE.**

Hint: Keep a lookout above for a mode of transport used by Native Americans.

Track down the Cosmic Pathway by the Hayden Sphere. Locate the sign explaining how many millions of years a single step equals on the pathway.

☐ **HAVE YOUR PHOTO SNAPPED TAKING A BIG STRIDE HERE, "TRAVELING" THROUGH MILLIONS OF YEARS IN A SINGLE STEP.**

CENTRAL PARK

SPECIAL AGENTS MUST BE IN TOP-NOTCH SHAPE. THIS MISSION WILL TEST YOUR PHYSICAL STRENGTH. HOW LONG CAN YOU STAY ON YOUR FEET TRACKING DOWN CLUES?

Central Park, a.k.a. New York's backyard, is massive, about the size of 630 football fields. It would be pretty difficult to see the entire place in one day. Don't worry if you can't find all the clues, you can still earn enough to become a special agent. Don't try to rush through the park though, because **IF you do happen to complete all the clues, then you can start counting park benches - Central Park has around 9,000 of them!**

- EQUESTRIAN STATUES
- HORSE-DRAWN CARRIAGES
- LAMPPOST
- DELACORTE CLOCK
- LENNON'S MOSAIC
- BETHESDA TERRACE
- 'ALICE' STATUE
- ANDERSEN STATUE
- BELVEDERE CASTLE
- THE OBELISK

As you stroll through the park, remain on point and find:

☐ **A STATUE OF A MAN RIDING A HORSE**

☐ **PEOPLE RIDING IN A HORSE-DRAWN CARRIAGE (10 POINTS MAX)**

1 *POINT EACH*

If you lose your way while in the park, no worries, because you can always locate a lamppost to help get you back on track. Park planners installed lampposts with small numbers inscribed on them listing the closest cross-street in the first few numbers.

☐ **TRACK DOWN A NUMBERED LAMPPOST.**

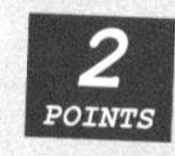

5
9
0
7

7220

☐ **LOCATE THIS CLOCK BY THE CHILDREN'S ZOO. WHICH ANIMALS ARE PLAYING THE VIOLIN AND THE DRUM?**

2 POINTS

☐ **FIND THIS MOSAIC* IN AN AREA CALLED "STRAWBERRY FIELDS." WHAT IS THE WORD AT THE CENTER?**

2 POINTS

John Lennon, a member of the famous band "The Beatles," once lived near this area of Central Park. This mosaic serves as a memorial to Lennon, who died in 1980. The title of one of his most famous songs, where he sings about a peaceful world, is the word at the mosaic's center.

*Mosaic = a design made from tiny pieces of glass or stone

Make your way to one of Central Park's most famous fountains: Bethesda Fountain. Once at the fountain, turn so you're facing the terrace.

THEN, HUNT AROUND THE STAIRS AND TERRACE TO FIND THESE ANIMALS:

☐ **A DEER**

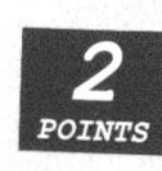

☐ **BIRDS IN THE FOREST**

☐ **AN OWL**

my notes:

Hunt down the *Alice In Wonderland* statue near Conservatory Water. Take two photos:

☐ **IN THE FIRST, SOMEONE ON YOUR TEAM MUST SIT ON TOP OF ONE OF THE MUSHROOMS.** 2 POINTS

☐ **IN THE SECOND, SOMEONE MUST KNEEL UNDERNEATH ONE OF THE MUSHROOMS.** 2 POINTS

Find the quirky lines from a poem by Lewis Carroll (the author of *Alice*). The poem resembles the song, "Twinkle Twinkle Little Star," but instead of the verses reading, "Twinkle twinkle little star," and "Like a diamond in the sky," Carroll changed two of the words.

☐ **WHICH TWO WORDS OF THESE TWO VERSES DID CARROLL CHANGE?** 3 POINTS

Nearby, track down the statue of Hans Christian Andersen, author of such tales as *The Little Mermaid, The Emperor's New Clothes*, and *The Ugly Duckling*.

☐ **HAVE YOUR PHOTO TAKEN SITTING BESIDE ANDERSEN AND PRETENDING TO READ THE BOOK IN HIS HAND.** 2 POINTS

☐ **BONUS: WHAT BOOK ARE YOU "READING"?**

Trek to Central Park's "castle," Belvedere Castle (near Turtle Pond). Although not a true castle, this place serves as a favorite wedding spot, and since the early 1900's, the National Weather Service has tracked official weather info such as wind speed and direction from here.

☐ **FIND THE CASTLE'S WIND VANE.**

Track down the dragon-like creature lurking in the glass.

☐ **HOW MANY FEET DOES IT HAVE?**

Locate Central Park's obelisk (near the Metropolitan Museum of Art). This 3500-year-old tower was hauled all the way from Egypt to New York in the 1800's.

☐ **HAVE YOUR PHOTO SNAPPED WITH THIS ANCIENT "SKYSCRAPER."**

METROPOLITAN MUSEUM OF ART

The Metropolitan Museum of Art (a.k.a* the "Met") measures over **TWO MILLION** square feet. (One square foot = 12 inches by 12 inches. Imagine larger floor tiles. They're usually 12 inches on each side, so imagine two million of those. That's the size of the Met.) Don't worry, you only have to explore a few parts of the museum to complete this mission.

AS YOU EXPLORE, STAY ON ALERT AND TRACK DOWN THE ITEMS LISTED ON THE NEXT PAGE. (20 POINTS MAX)

(Examples are included, although you don't necessarily have to locate these. For each point you must also report to your case officer what part of the world the artwork is from.)

*a.k.a. = "also known as"; it's a common term spies use to identify someone or something that goes by more than one name

- ART HUNT
- ROUND-THE-WORLD "TRAVEL"
- CUBICULUM NOCTURNUM
- TIFFANY GLASS
- PRESIDENT'S PAINTING
- ARMS & ARMOR
- DEGAS-MONET-VAN GOGH
- YOUR FAVORITE PIECES

☐ **ARTWORK OF KIDS YOUR AGE**

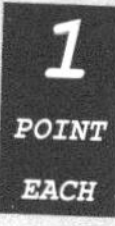

☐ **HALF-HUMAN/ HALF-ANIMAL SCULPTURES**

Hint: Track down exhibits from Egypt, Mesopotamia, and Greece to rack up points for this one.

☐ **MASKS**

my notes:

SPECIAL AGENTS SOMETIMES HAVE TO DROP EVERYTHING AND TRAVEL TO FAR-AWAY LANDS TO COMPLETE MISSIONS.

For the time being, we won't ask you to do that. We just want you to make it *appear* as if you have. **Inside lie three spaces which could easily pass for areas in foreign countries.**

Have your photo snapped in the three exhibits listed below, and maybe you can convince anyone viewing your photos that you ventured as far away as China for the day. *Be sure to read the three exhibit descriptions carefully - in case anyone starts asking questions about your "travels."

BEFORE LEAVING THE MET, HAVE YOUR PHOTO TAKEN IN:

2 POINTS

☐ **"CHINA"**
(The Chinese Garden Court)

2 POINTS

☐ **"EGYPT"**
(The Tomb of Perneb or Temple of Dendur)

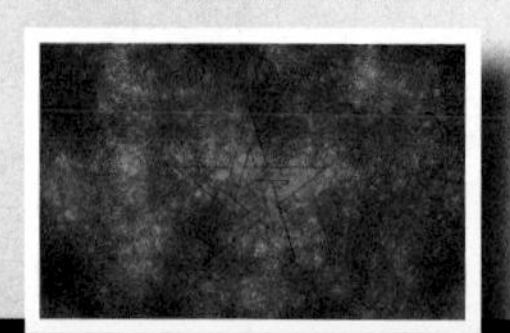

2 POINTS

☐ **"MOROCCO"**
(The Moroccan Court)

☐ **FIND THE CUBICULUM NOCTURNUM.** 2 POINTS

Try saying that title five-times-fast. ("Cubiculum Nocturnum" = bedroom.)

The eruption of Mount Vesuvius in the year 79 destroyed two cities and killed around 16,000 people in southern Italy. This structure gives us a glimpse of what southern Italy looked like almost 2,000 years ago.

Locate the stained glass art of Louis Tiffany and examine the title of this piece.

☐ **WHICH SEASON DID TIFFANY SHOW HERE?**

my notes:

....

....

Hunt down this famous painting.

☐ **WHICH PRESIDENT COMMANDS THE BOAT?** **2 POINTS**

Make your way to the Arms and Armor Court. Locate a helmet displayed like the one below.

☐ **MAKE IT APPEAR AS IF YOUR HEAD IS INSIDE THE HELMET, RE-CREATING A PHOTO LIKE THIS.** 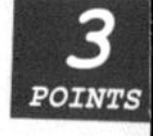

If the museum has changed the display of helmets, then earn points by having your photo snapped next to the warriors on horseback on display.

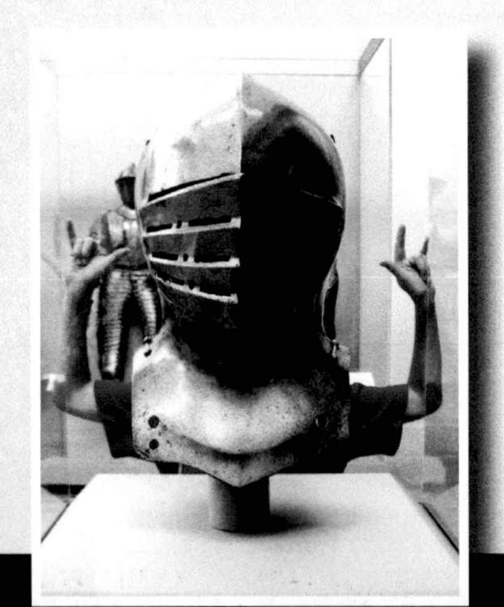

For the next three, you'll need to track down these works and locate their titles for the answers. (We listed the artist's last name below his work.)

☐ **HOW OLD IS DEGAS' DANCER?** — **2 POINTS**

☐ **WHAT MONUMENT SITS ON THE RIVERBANK?** — **2 POINTS**

☐ **WHAT TYPE OF GRAIN DID VAN GOGH PAINT IN THE FIELD?** — **2 POINTS**

☐ **IF YOU WERE AN ART COLLECTOR, WHICH THREE PIECES IN THE MUSEUM WOULD YOU WANT TO ADD TO YOUR COLLECTION?** — **3 POINTS**

☐ **WHICH THREE PIECES DO YOU THINK TOOK THE MOST SKILL TO CREATE?** — **3 POINTS**

my notes:

mission: #4 date:__________

MUSEUM OF MODERN ART

DALI ("Dah-lee")

WARHOL

PICASSO

Hunt down a gift shop for a postcard rack of the museum's works. **Together with your case officer, select a few postcards of interesting works to track down inside.** Your case officer sets the number of points per postcard.

____ POINT(S) EACH

☐ FIND ARTWORK BY THE THREE ARTISTS ABOVE WHOSE QUOTES FOLLOW. (TEN POINTS MAX.)

"I always like to see if the art across the street is better than mine." -Andy Warhol

☐ COMPARE WARHOL'S ART WITH THAT OF THE OTHERS AROUND NEARBY. WHO'S THE BETTER ARTIST - WARHOL OR THE OTHERS?

TOTAL POINTS

- POSTCARD HUNT
- DALI-PICASSO-WARHOL: ARTWORK & QUOTES
- KAHLO'S SELF-PORTRAIT
- MONET
- VAN GOGH
- ROUSSEAU
- UNUSUAL ARTWORK

"The world today doesn't make sense, so why should I paint pictures that do?" -Pablo Picasso

☐ FROM YOUR POINT OF VIEW, DOES PICASSO'S ART MAKE SENSE?

1 POINT

"Drawing is the honesty of the art. There is no possibility of cheating. It is either good or bad." -Salvador Dali

☐ IN YOUR OPINION, IS DALI'S ART GOOD OR BAD?

1 POINT

Track down a self-portrait of the artist Frida Kahlo. Examine her facial features in this photo and then in the painting(s) you find.

☐ DO YOU BELIEVE KAHLO DID A GOOD JOB PAINTING HERSELF?

my notes:

If you can complete the next two clues, then you truly have the keen eyes necessary for a special agent. Examine these two images.

☐ **THEN, TRACK DOWN THE FULL COLOR VERSIONS IN THE MUSEUM.**

Hint: The artist of the work above: Claude Monet (Monet = "Mo-nay"). The artist of the work below: Vincent Van Gogh (Gogh = "Go").

Track down *The Gypsy* by the artist Rousseau ("Roo-so").

☐ **WHAT ANIMAL PROWLS BESIDE OF THE SLEEPING GYPSY?**

2 *POINTS*

☐ **WHAT THREE PIECES OF ART DID YOU FIND THE MOST UNUSUAL?**

3 *POINTS*

my notes:

ROCKEFELLER CENTER

John Rockefeller, Sr. & "Johnny Rock"

Rockefeller Center is NYC's "city within a city," stretching between 48th and 51st Streets. It was built in the 1930's by John Rockefeller, Jr. (known as "Johnny Rock" to his school buddies), the son of the world's first billionaire, John Rockefeller, Sr.

Johnny Rock's dad was a hard worker from the beginning. For many kids, his/her birthday is, hands-down, the most important day of the year, but not for Rockefeller. Although his birthday was July 8 (1839), September 26 was his gold-star day: the day he got his first job. Rockefeller would go on to make billions of dollars building an oil empire and gave about half a billion dollars to charity.

TOTAL POINTS

- RADIO CITY MUSIC HALL
- TV STUDIO
- FLAGS OF ALL NATIONS
- WISDOM RELIEF
- PROMETHEUS
- ATLAS STATUE
- BRITISH EMPIRE DOOR
- THE REAL JAMES BOND

Track down the neon sign for Radio City Music Hall, NYC's famous performance hall.

☐ **FIND THIS SIGN REPRESENTING ENTERTAINERS ON THE EXTERIOR.** 2 POINTS

Scan the area around you for another neon sign, this time for a TV network.

☐ **WHAT TV NETWORK'S STUDIO ALSO LIES ON THIS STREET?** 2 POINTS

Locate the Flags of All Nations.

☐ **NAME AT LEAST 10 FLAGS IN THE LINE-UP.**

During holidays, only the U.S. flag flies. If visiting during a holiday (or other special occasion when the Flags of All Nations aren't flying) then earn points by having your photo snapped by the flags.

Note: If your team visits the "Top of The Rock," don't miss mission #7.

ATLAS

WISDOM

PROMETHEUS

Find the "Wisdom" relief. (Relief = a flat sculpture.)

☐ **WHAT IS THE MESSAGE IN THE SCULPTURE?**

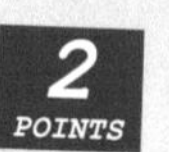

☐ **TAKE A PHOTO OF ONE OF THE CITY'S MOST POPULAR STATUES: THE TITAN PROMETHEUS.**

To make it a bit challenging, the photo above shows only the top part of the gold titan. (Titans were a type of Greek god.)

☐ **FIND THE STATUE OF ANOTHER TITAN, "ATLAS," HOLDING THE HEAVENS.**

Track down the door of the British Empire Building. In days past, Britain ruled lands in every corner of the globe, from Canada and the Caribbean to India and Australia (to name only a few). The saying was, "the sun never sets on the British Empire." Examine the door's figures, symbolizing the industries of the empire.

☐ **FIND THREE TYPES OF ANIMALS ON THE DOOR.**

The Real James Bond

James Bond (movie version)

James Bond (real-life version)

Most people stroll past the site near your earlier clue (the titan "Atlas") not even realizing its story as **one of recent history's most important spy sites**. Here, at **630 Fifth Avenue**, at a spot simply referred to as **"Room 3603,"** the British set up a spy HQ during World War II.* The British spymaster in charge of Room 3603, a man by the name of **William Stephenson**, went by the codename **"Intrepid"** and was a **real-life James Bond**. Bond's creator (an author by the name of Ian Fleming) called Intrepid the "real thing."

"Fast on his feet" does not even begin to describe Intrepid. Before becoming a spymaster he already had a long list of accomplishments that included: fighter pilot, championship boxer, and millionaire.

Stephenson took to the skies after only *five* hours of flight training, quickly achieving the title "ace" for taking down **26 enemy planes**. Not even getting shot down and thrown in enemy prison camp could slow him: **he risked death and managed to make a daring escape**.

Within a few years, Intrepid managed to build a manufacturing business, **one that presented the perfect cover to spy on the weapons factories of the evil Nazis**. Britain's Prime Minister, quite impressed with Intrepid's slick spying skills, wasted no time in sending Intrepid off to the U.S., with a "cover" job of "Passport Control Officer." **His real mission: lead a spy ring to collect as much top secret intel as possible against the Axis powers**. He set up "Camp X," the first spy school in North America. One of the trainees, according to some reports: Ian Fleming (James Bond's creator). Intrepid even helped bust an Axis spy ring bold enough to carry out operations on U.S. soil.

Ian Fleming

After the war the Americans awarded him with the Presidential Medal of Merit and the British gave him the coveted title of "Knight" - not bad for someone merely doing paperwork as a Passport Control Officer.

*In World War II (1939-1945), the "Allies" (led by Great Britain, France, the U.S., China, and Russia) battled the "Axis" (led by Germany, Japan, and Italy).

mission: #6 date:__________

GRAND CENTRAL TERMINAL

SPECIAL AGENTS MUST ALWAYS HAVE THEIR EYES PEELED FOR INTELLIGENCE: CLUES AND CRITICAL INFO THAT OTHERS OFTEN OVERLOOK. CAN YOU FIND THE 'INTEL' NEEDED TO COMPLETE THIS MISSION?

Welcome to the largest train terminal in the world. At last count, this place had 67 train tracks, and today you'll be one of about 750,000 people who pass through here every day.

TOTAL POINTS

- VANDERBILT SYMBOLS
- TERMINAL CLOCKS
- CONSTELLATIONS
- CEILING SQUARE
- WHISPERING GALLERY

Outside

VANDERBILT

Cornelius Vanderbilt, one of the richest men in American history, made a fortune building railroads in the U.S. He constructed a railroad terminal on this very spot in 1871, but Vanderbilt's structure was torn down and eventually replaced by Grand Central Terminal in 1913. However, many reminders of the Vanderbilt family remain.

HOW MANY CAN YOU FIND?

2 POINTS EACH

- ☐ **CORNELIUS VANDERBILT STATUE**
- ☐ **VANDERBILT EAGLE**
- ☐ **VANDERBILT AVENUE SIGN**

Inside keep a look out for the Vanderbilt symbol, an acorn (only, it sometimes may appear a bit like a pineapple).

One of the most important things when it comes to traveling: knowing the correct time. (Rumor has it that Grand Central's trains actually leave one minute past their scheduled departure - to help out any last-minute passengers sprinting to catch their trains.)

☐ **HUNT DOWN TWO CLOCKS, ONE OUTSIDE THE TERMINAL AND ONE INSIDE.**

Inside

☐ **FIND THE "REVERSED" CONSTELLATIONS.**

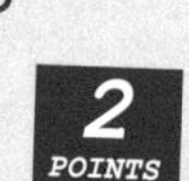

At first glance this appears like a pretty good re-creation of the constellations that dot the night-time sky. However, for those of you who closely examine the sky at night, you'll notice that these constellations are actually painted in reverse - the opposite of how they truly appear up high in the heavens.

my notes:

If you can find the next object, you definitely have the sharp skills necessary for a special agent. Examine the areas around the constellation painting's four corners.

☐ **FIND THE SMALL DARK SQUARE.**

In the 1990's the ceiling underwent a major cleaning. The cleaners left this here as a reminder of how dirty the area appeared prior to cleaning, thanks to residue from cigarette smoke.

Word on the street has it that in the terminal lies a "whispering gallery" - just outside a restaurant called the Oyster Bar. By the restaurant, find the curved ceiling of this "gallery." Position a team member so that he/she is standing in the diagonal corner of the archway from you.

☐ **WHISPER FACING THE WALL AND SEE IF YOUR VOICE TRAVELS ACROSS THE CURVED WALL TO REACH YOUR TEAMMATE.**

3
POINTS

(You'll probably see other people "testing" this as well.)

mission: #7 date:__________

EMPIRE STATE vs. TOP OF THE ROCK

AGENTS MUST HAVE SHARP EYES TO SPOT THINGS FROM A DISTANCE. IN THE FIELD, SOMETIMES YOU CAN'T DEPEND ON ZOOM LENSES OR BINOCULARS FOR ASSISTANCE, JUST YOUR OWN TWO EYES.

The Empire State Building and Rockefeller Center's Top-of-the-Rock are two of the major contenders for the title of NYC's "best lookout point." Put your observation skills to the test atop one (or both) of these spots to earn points.

TOTAL POINTS

FIND:

- ☐ CHRYSLER BUILDING
- ☐ STATUE OF LIBERTY
- ☐ BROOKLYN BRIDGE
- ☐ TEN YELLOW TAXI CABS

MORE ON THE NEXT PAGE...

ONE WORLD TRADE CENTER

On September 11, 2001, terrorists attacked the United States. In New York they flew two airplanes into the Twin Towers of the World Trade Center. They flew another plane into the Pentagon (the nation's military headquarters) in Washington, D.C. and had a fourth plane destined for the U.S. Capitol. (The passengers and crew of this plane managed to overtake the terrorists, and the plane crashed into a field in Pennsylvania.) Thousands died in the attack, including hundreds of emergency workers (firefighters, police officers, and other first responders).

The Twin Towers

The National September 11 Memorial stands in remembrance to the victims of 9/11 and as a symbol of how the country stood united following the attacks. One World Trade Center, the tallest building in the U.S., towers above the city and represents the strength and spirit of New York and the nation.

The National
September 11 Memorial

See the Twin Towers in these two designs? (The left, the seal of the Navy ship the USS *New York*; the right, a New York Police Department memorial patch.)

BROOKLYN BRIDGE

The Brooklyn Bridge connects two of the city's boroughs* together, Manhattan and Brooklyn.

The word "Manhattan" comes from the Lenape ("Leh-nah-pay") term "Manna Hata." The Lenape were the

*Borough = one of the five main sections of NYC (Manhattan, Brooklyn, Queens, the Bronx, and Staten Island)

- CROSS THE BRIDGE
- THE ROEBLING FAMILY
- LOVE LOCKS
- TOWER DATE

TOTAL POINTS

Native Americans living in this area when the Europeans landed on its shores in the 1500's.

LAPOWINSA, Lenape Chief (1737)

Before George Washington became the first U.S. president, he served as Commander-in-Chief in the Revolutionary War, where the Americans battled the British for independence. (The British, who initially controlled New York after the Dutch gave it up, named the city after the Duke of York.) Brooklyn was the site of a major battle of the Revolutionary War. Back then, Washington would've crossed this waterway, the East River, via boat. Today, 120,000 vehicles and 4,000 pedestrians cross it every day using the Brooklyn Bridge.

WASHINGTON

☐ **CROSS THE BROOKLYN BRIDGE.** **3** *POINTS*

Nowadays you can cross for free, but had you been around when the bridge first opened in the late 1800's, you would have had to pay a penny to walk across, a nickel to ride a horse, or a dime to cross in a horse-led wagon.

Before completing your journey to the other side...

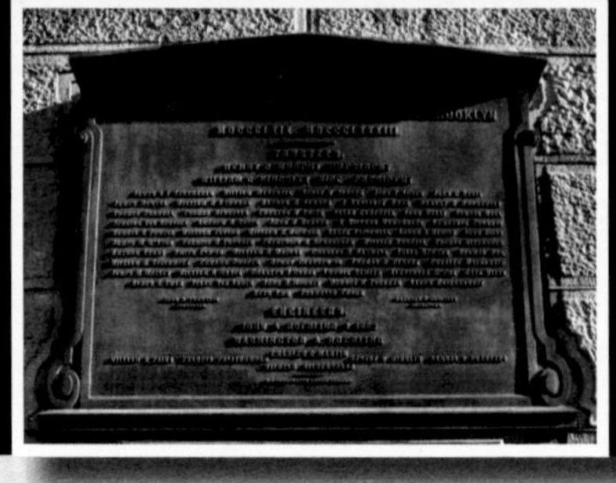

☐ LOCATE THIS PLAQUE ON ONE OF THE TOWERS.

2 POINTS

Three members of the same family were behind the bridge's construction. Read the plaque to uncover the names of the bridge's chief engineers, men by the last name of "Roebling."

☐ WHAT WERE THEIR NAMES?

2 POINTS

Back in the 1800's bridge construction was one dangerous job. At least 20 people died while working on the bridge, and the first to meet his end was one of the men whose name (beginning with "J"), you just found. His foot was crushed even before construction officially began, and he soon died of tetanus*.

☐ WHAT WAS THE NAME OF THE THIRD FAMILY MEMBER?

2 POINTS

Hint: Track down another nearby plaque, containing an image of the bridge, as well as the family's history, for the answer.

*Tetanus = a bacteria that enters your body through wounds (Thankfully today we have tetanus vaccines to protect us.)

☐ **FIND A LOVE LOCK.** 2 POINTS

Couples write their names or initials on the lock, lock it in place on the bridge, then throw the lock's key into the water, and wish for eternal love. Because the locks are sometimes removed from the bridge (it's actually against the rules to attach "love locks"), if you can't find any, earn points by snapping a photo of the New York skyline from the bridge.

The bridge was completed in 1883.

☐ **HOWEVER, THE BRIDGE'S TOWERS WERE COMPLETED A FEW YEARS BEFORE, IN 187_.** 2 POINTS

Hint: To uncover the year, as you cross the bridge towers, keep your head tilted up, on the lookout for this year carved in stone.

The bridge may be undergoing improvements when you visit. If you can't complete the clues because something is blocked, use this clue to make up your points.

☐ **HUNT DOWN AN AMERICAN FLAG FLYING ON THE BRIDGE.** ___ POINTS

mission: #9 date:__________

STATUE OF LIBERTY

The Statue of Liberty was a grand gift from France to the U.S. in honor of the anniversary of America's independence from Britain.

Back in the days when Liberty was constructed, the idea that citizens should control the government (and not, for example, be controlled by a single ruler, like a king, queen, or emperor) was quite uncommon. Nations, like France, saw that America's democracy "experiment" could work. Today "Lady Liberty" serves as a grand welcome to New York's harbor.

TOTAL POINTS

- TABLET DATE
- PENNY INSCRIPTION
- COPPER'S THICKNESS
- LIBERTY'S CROWN
- FORT'S POINTS
- THE WORLD NEWSPAPER
- BARTHOLDI, EIFFEL, AND PULITZER

AGENTS MUST HAVE A SHARP EYE FOR DETAIL. THEY ALWAYS NEED TO HAVE THEIR EYES PEELED FOR THE TINIEST CLUES - CRITICAL INFO THAT OTHERS USUALLY MISS. IT'S TIME TO PUT YOUR SKILLS TO THE TEST.

Find the perfect spot to analyze the tablet Liberty holds in her hand. The tablet contains three lines: an important date. The last line reads "1776" in Roman numerals. (The ancient Romans originally used Roman numerals, and we still use them today on things like clocks and monuments.)

☐ **WHAT DO THE FIRST TWO LINES READ?** 2 POINTS

Use this chart if you need help in decoding the Roman numeral on the second line.

1	2	3	4	5	6	7	8	9	10
I	II	III	IV	V	VI	VII	VIII	IX	X

The statue is made of copper - copper that has weathered over the years and changed colors due to rain and air. The statue's copper layer is only two pennies' thick. Find two pennies.

☐ **WHAT WORD IS INSCRIBED ON YOUR COINS' FRONT LEFT SIDE?**

my notes:

☐ **BONUS: HOLD THE COINS TOGETHER TO SEE HOW THICK THE STATUE'S COPPER LAYER IS.**

1 *POINT*

☐ **HOW MANY POINTS DOES THE CROWN ATOP LIBERTY'S HEAD HAVE?**

Some say the number represents liberty's ability to reach across all the seas and all the continents.

Here at one of the nation's busiest ports, a number of forts were constructed to guard the harbor, including the one which stands on Lady Liberty's island (Fort Wood). The fort is in the shape of a star.

☐ **HOW MANY POINTS DOES THE FORT'S STAR HAVE?**

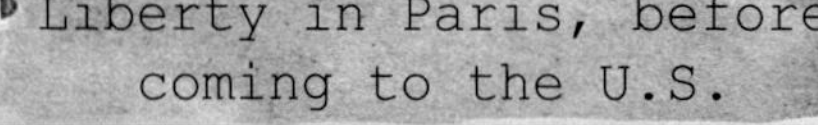

Liberty in Paris, before coming to the U.S.

The French designed and paid for the statue (the Americans paid for the statue's pedestal). They shipped Liberty all the way across the Atlantic Ocean in crates, with the statue broken down into 350 pieces and completely reassembled here. The Americans at first had trouble raising enough money to pay for the pedestal. So, *The New York World* newspaper devised a clever plan to drum up enough funds. People and groups who donated money would have their names published on the front page of the newspaper. Problem solved.

☐ **FIND THE NEW YORK WORLD NEWSPAPER (ALSO CALLED SIMPLY 'THE WORLD') ON DISPLAY IN THE VISITOR CENTER.** **2 POINTS**

ON THE ISLAND FIND STATUES OF THREE PEOPLE IMPORTANT TO LIBERTY'S CONSTRUCTION:

☐ **FREDERIC BARTHOLDI** *("Bar-tol-dee")* (the sculptor)

☐ **GUSTAVE EIFFEL** (*"Goo-stahv Eye-fell"*) (the designer of Liberty's frame and of France's Eiffel Tower)

☐ **JOSEPH PULITZER** (publisher of *The New York World* newspaper) **1 POINT**

mission: #10 date:___________

ELLIS ISLAND MUSEUM

Millions of immigrants to the U.S. (over 10 million to be exact) began their new lives as "Americans" at this very spot. These new Americans had spent weeks traveling to reach the promise of a better life in the United States. Four out of every 10 Americans have at least one ancestor who came to America through Ellis Island.

☐ **FIND THE DISPLAY OF IMMIGRANT LUGGAGE.**

Imagine you had to move to a new country with only a few pieces of luggage.

☐ **WHAT WOULD YOU PACK IN YOUR BAGS?**

TOTAL POINTS

- LUGGAGE DISPLAY
- LUGGAGE QUESTION
- ANNIE MOORE
- STAIRS OF SEPARATION
- PHOTOS: OF IMMIGRANTS YOUR AGE, OF IMMIGRANTS YOUR CASE OFFICER'S AGE

2 POINTS

☐ **TRACK DOWN THE STATUE OF ANNIE MOORE.**

The first immigrant to pass through Ellis Island, she arrived from Ireland on New Year's Day, 1892. (Immigrants arrived at Ellis Island from 1892 to 1954.)

☐ **HOW MANY SECTIONS DO THE "STAIRS OF SEPARATION" HAVE?**

☐ **IF AN IMMIGRANT WAS "DETAINED" (HELD BACK), WHICH STAIR SECTION DID HE/SHE USE?**

2 POINTS

☐ **FIND PHOTOS OF AT LEAST THREE ELLIS ISLAND IMMIGRANTS WHO APPEAR TO BE YOUR AGE.**

☐ **FIND PHOTOS OF AT LEAST THREE ELLIS ISLAND IMMIGRANTS WHO APPEAR TO BE THE AGE OF YOUR CASE OFFICER(S).**

mission: #11 date:__________

SIGHTS OF NYC

As your team crosses these famous sights off your "to see" list, you can rack up some serious points.

HAVE YOUR PHOTO SNAPPED AT THESE ATTRACTIONS:

☐ **CHRYSLER BUILDING**

☐ **WALL STREET BULL**

This aggressive bull stands ready to charge full speed ahead, but for the moment pauses in a small park in the city's Financial District.

TOTAL POINTS

- CHRYSLER BUILDING
- WALL STREET BULL
- HIGH LINE
- TIMES SQUARE
- CONEY ISLAND
- USS INTREPID

☐ HIGH LINE

2 *POINTS*

(a park set up on an abandoned railway bridge)

☐ TIMES SQUARE

One of the world's most visited tourist attractions, this place is filled with two things: big bright neon signs and people (care to start counting…the bright signs, that is).

☐ CONEY ISLAND

Home to amusement parks, a beach, and a world-famous hot dog eating contest. (The 2014 winner ate 61 hotdogs in 10 minutes.)

☐ USS INTREPID

(part of the Intrepid Sea, Air & Space Museum)

mission: #12 date:__________

ANYTIME MISSIONS

THE BEST AGENTS HAVE A HIGH LEVEL OF SOMETHING CALLED "SITUATIONAL AWARENESS." THESE QUICK-WITTED AGENTS PAY CLOSE ATTENTION TO THEIR SURROUNDINGS - READY TO COLLECT CRITICAL INTELLIGENCE AND RESPOND TO DANGEROUS SITUATIONS. HAVING EXCELLENT "SITUATIONAL AWARENESS" (SA FOR SHORT) MEANS ALWAYS BEING "ON ALERT."

These missions will test your SA. Don't let your guard down as you wander around New York, or you may miss a chance to win points.

NEW YORK FOOD

Try some of the food that NYC is famous for. To receive each point, you must have your photo snapped taking a big bite (or take the photo of your case officer(s) doing the same thing).

TEN POINTS MAX FOR THIS PART.

☐ **BAGEL** — 1 POINT EACH

☐ **HOT DOG** — 1 POINT EACH

TOTAL POINTS

☐ PIZZA — 1 POINT EACH

☐ PRETZEL

☐ BONUS: LOCATE A FOOD CART VENDOR WHO'S SMILING. — 1 POINT

New York is a multi-cultural city, full of people from all over the world. According to some sources, around **800** languages are spoken here. Listen up for languages other than English.

☐ ONE POINT EVERY FOREIGN LANGUAGE YOU AND YOUR CASE OFFICER CAN IDENTIFY. (TEN POINTS MAX)

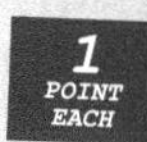

☐ RIDE IN A YELLOW TAXI CAB

In NYC, the rhythms of street musicians often fill the air - in Central Park, on city walks, and in the subway.

☐ **EARN ONE POINT FOR EACH STREET MUSICIAN YOU SPOT. (TEN POINTS MAX)**

1 POINT EACH

For each point, you must also correctly identify the instrument played.

AS YOU TREK AROUND THE CITY, KEEP YOUR EYES PEELED FOR THESE FAMOUS STREET SIGNS. (TEN POINTS MAX)

☐ **BROADWAY**

☐ **5TH AVENUE**

☐ **WALL STREET**

ANYTIME MISSIONS: BONUS

COME ACROSS A MONUMENT OR EXHIBIT THAT'S CLOSED? NOT ENOUGH TIME IN NYC? HAVE NO FEAR, USE THESE MISSIONS TO ACHIEVE YOUR GOAL. YOUR CASE OFFICER SETS THE POINTS.

☐ TOGETHER WITH YOUR CASE OFFICER, PLAN YOUR ROUTES IN NEW YORK'S SUBWAY.

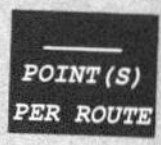

HUNT DOWN A JERSEY FROM EACH OF THE CITY'S SPORTS TEAMS.

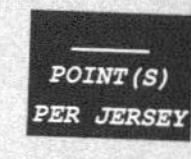

☐ BASEBALL: METS, YANKEES

☐ BASKETBALL: NETS, KNICKS

☐ WOMEN'S BASKETBALL: LIBERTY

☐ FOOTBALL: GIANTS, JETS

☐ HOCKEY: ISLANDERS, RANGERS

☐ SOCCER: NYC FC, RED BULLS

☐ WOMEN'S SOCCER: SKY BLUE FC

ANSWER KEY

Once an answer is submitted, your case officer can check it here. If you peek at this answer key before submitting a final answer, you won't receive any points for that clue. Most clues do not have one correct answer, for those that do, here are the answers. (Please see page 58 for the Pre-Arrival Brief answer.)

#1 Natural History Museum: The statue is Theodore Roosevelt. The extinct bird: a dodo bird. The island name of the Moai figures: Easter Island/Rapa Nui. "Lucy" is 3.18 million years old. The Beatles sung the song she's named after.

#2 Central Park: On the clock, the hippo plays the violin and the penguin plays the drum. The word at the center of the mosaic: Imagine. In the 'Alice' statue, Star is BAT. Diamond is TEA TRAY. In the Andersen statue, the book is 'The Ugly Duckling.' At Belvedere Castle, the creature has two feet.

#3 The Met: The season in Tiffany's glass: Autumn. George Washington commands the boat. Degas' dancer is 14. Monet painted London's Parliament. Van Gogh painted wheat.

#4 Museum of Modern Art: The animal beside the gypsy: a lion.

#5 Rockefeller Center: The TV studio near Radio City: NBC. The 'Wisdom' message: Wisdom and knowledge shall be the stability of thy times. Three types of animals in the British Empire door: bird, fish, sheep.

#6 Brooklyn Bridge: The names on the plaque: John and Washington Roebling. The name of the third family member: Emily Roebling. The year on the tower: 1875.

#7 Statue of Liberty: The tablet's first two lines: July 4. 'Liberty' is inscribed on the side of the penny. Liberty's crown has 7 points. The fort's star has 11 points.

#8 Ellis Island: The stairs have 3 sections. Immigrants who were detained used the steps' center section.

NOTE: the information in this book was accurate as of December 2014. We hope that you won't find anything outdated related to the clues. If you do find that something has changed, please email us at info@ScavengerHuntAdventures.com to kindly let us know.

THANK YOU FOR SELECTING THIS BOOK.

We hope you enjoyed the missions! Comments, suggestions? Contact us at info@ScavengerHuntAdventures.com or on Facebook. We are a family-owned business, and we'd love to hear from you.

THE FINAL MISSION

Case officers, please visit
scavengerhuntadventures.com/bonus
(all lowercase letters)

☐ **JOIN 'THE INSIDER' (OUR EMAIL LIST)**
You'll get a special bonus mission for this city plus our free e-book, *The Museum Spy*.

PLEASE HELP SPREAD THE WORD

We're a small family business and would be thrilled if you **left a review online*** or **recommended our books to a friend.**

Our books: Paris, London, Amsterdam, Rome, NYC, D.C., Barcelona, Florence, St. Augustine, with more coming!

*We can't mention the site name here, but it begins with "AM"!

A BIG THANK YOU

Thank you for supporting our family-owned business.

Mom writes, Dad serves in the military, and Jr. helps "research" our books. **Without you this series wouldn't be possible.**

Thank YOU!

Catherine

Answer for the Pre-Arrival Brief:

IMAGE CREDITS Images of paintings which do not require image crediting are not listed. The two digit numbers are the file license number (links below), links to Flickr photographer sites are also below. License for all Flickr photos is Creative Commons 2.0.(T=Top, B=Bottom, M=Middle; L=Left, R=Right, C=Center); WIKIMEDIA: p.4: NASA; p.5-Theshibboleth-1.2; p.6-T-J.M. Luijit-2.5; BL-Library of Congress (LOC); p.7-LOC; p.8-TR-Shank27-3.0;ML-1.2;BL-Mike Peel, mikepeel.net-4.0;BR-Zac Wolf-2.5;p.9-TL- JM Luijt-2.5;TR-Raul654-1.2; B-Futureman1199-3.0; p.10 T-Bradenfox-3.0;B-Suraj-3.0; p.11-T-Netherlands Natl Archive;B-Martin Thoma-1.0; p.13-C-CZ Marlin 1.0; p.14-M-Licentie afbeeldingen Beeld en Geluidwiki; B-Jim Henderson-1.0; p.16-BL-Captain Tucker-3.0;BR-Leonard G-1.0; p.17-TLC-Daderot-3.0;TLR-Pumpkin Sky-3.0; p.19-LL- Pierre Selim-3.0; RR-Shooting Brooklyn 2.5; p.20 China & Egpyt Stamps-Kristoferb-3.0; p.21-B-Sailko-3.0; p.22-L-Agnostic Preachers Kid-3.0; p.24-R-Peter Zeliznak;C-Vea y Lea; p.28-L-David Shankbone(see website below) p.29-M-Laslo Varga-1.2;p.30-R-Balon Greyjoy;B-CGP Grey(see website below); p.32-Eric Baetscher-1.2;p.33-M-Ari Armstrong-3.0;B-Farragutful-3.0;p.34-TL-Ingfbruno-3.0;TR-Lesekreis-3.0;C-Arnoldius-3.0;p.37-TR-David Shankbone(see website below);MR-Daniel Schwen-4.0;p.37-BL- Suiseiseki-3.0;p.38-T-Lesekreis-3.0;B-Jeff Mock-1.2;p.40-Suiseiseki-3.0; p.44-Derek Jensen(Tysto); p.47-BR-Rafael Isla-4.0; p.48-Ingfbruno; p.49-B-All from Popular Science; p.51-L-Westport Wiki-3.0; p.51-T-Terabass; p.54-BR-JSquish FLICKR: p.6-BR-Wendel F.; p.9-MR-Jim Bowen; p.11-M-Tony Hisgett; p.12-Ed Yourdon; p.13-L-Tracy Elizabeth;R-Carlis Dambrans; p.14-T-Eric Salard; p.15-T-Frank Kovalcheck;B-Shawnzrossi; p.16-T-Tony Hisgett; p.17-TL-Benson Kua;B-Boston Public Library; p.18-M-Alkali Soaps; R-Rosemaniakos; p.19-LC-Rosemaniakos; RC-Alkali Soaps; p.20-All flags-Free Grunge Textures;Morocco Stamp-John Rawlinson; p.22-B-Sabra Smith; p.29-T-CJN212; p.29-B-Sparkly Kate; p.30-TL-Esparto Palma;TC-Goetzihh; p.31-TL-Allan Wu;B-Paul Baack; p.35-Flickr4Jazz;p.36-L-Erik Kilby;R-Sharat Ganapati; p.39-BR-David Conner;TL-Kim CarpenterNJ;TR-Anthony Quintano;p.42-T-Lolas Big Adventure; p.44-T-Betsy Weber;p.46-R-Boston Public Library;p.49-T-Shelley Panzarella; p.50-TR-David Ohmer;BR-Mike Boucher; p.51-M-Boston Public Library;B-Chris Paul 2014; p.52-Muffet;p.53-T-The Pizza Review;B-Pascal Subtil;p.54-T-Nan Palermo;M-Peter Bellis;BL-Kumweni;p.55-Prayitno Flickr User & Other Website Links: Example: http://www.flickr.com/photos/79865753@N00 = 79865753@N00; Alkali Soaps: alkalisoaps; Allan Wu: arabani; Angela N.: aon; Anthony Quintano: quintanomedia; Betsy Weber: betsyweber; Boston Public Library: boston_public_library; CGP Grey: http://www.cgpgrey.com/; Chris Paul 2014: 107489497@N06; CJN212: 24940787@N02; Dave Conner: conner395; David Ohmer: the-o; David Shankbone: http://shankbone.org/; Ed Yourdon: people/72098626@N00; Eric Kilby: people/8749778@N06; Eric Salard: people/16103393@N05; Esparta Palma: esparto; Flickr 4 Jazz: flickr4jazz; Frank Kovalchek: 72213316@N00; Free Grunge Textures: 80497449@N04; Greyloch: greyloch/4288753415; Jason Eppink: jasoneppink; Jim Bowen: jamiedfw; John Rawlinson: London; Karlis Dambrans: janitors; Kim Carpenter NJ: kim_carpenter_nj; Kumweni: 76338186@N03; Lola's Big Adventure: kokalola; Matt McDermott: matmcdermott; MCAD: 69184488@N06; Michael Grabios: mgrabois; Mike Boucher: 27722079@N04; Muffet: calliope; Nan Palermo: nanpalmero; Pascal Subtil: pascal_subtil; Paul Baack: paulbaack; Peter Bellis: video4net; Prayitno: prayitnophotography; Ralph and Jenny: ralphandjenny; Rosemania: rosemania; Rosemaniakos: rosemania/86741652; Sabra Smith: sabrasmith; Sharat Ganapati: people/75718896@N00; Shawnzrossi: shawnzlea; Shelley Panzarella: shelleyp; Sparkly Kate: sparklykate; Squirrel 83: squirrel02; The Pizza Review: thepizzareview; Tony Hisgett: hisgett; Tracy Elizabeth: tracyelizabeths; Wendel F: wendelf; Links to Licenses:1.0: http://creativecommons.org/licenses/by-sa/1.0/deed.en; 1.2: creativecommons.org/licenses/by-sa/1.2/deed.en; 1.5: creativecommons.org/licenses/by-sa/1.5/deed.en;2.0: creativecommons.org/licenses/by-sa/2.0/deed.en; 2.5: creativecommons.org/licenses/by-sa/2.5/deed.en; 3.0: creativecommons.org/licenses/by-sa/3.0/deed.en